Father Damien

38211

Father Damien

An Open Letter to the
Reverend Dr. Hyde of Honolulu from
Robert Louis Stevenson

[WITH A STATEMENT BY MRS. STEVENSON]

The Ave Maria Press
Notre Dame, Indiana
U. S. A.

Publisher's Preface.

THE constant demand for the far-famed "Open Letter" in durable rather than dainty form, but more especially the reiterated assertion that Stevenson regretted this production and would have recalled it had recall been possible, are the *raison d'être* of the present reprint. An American author of some repute has had the hardihood to declare in one of his books that "Stevenson did not really believe what he wrote, neither did he intend to write what he did. . . . Stevenson could not have been honest at heart when he wrote his letter to Dr. Hyde." It is well, perhaps, for this worthy that the pen of the man whom he thus defames is now powerless.

Feeling sure that some day when "in his resting grave" the defender of Father Damien would need to be defended himself, we took care several years ago to secure from Mrs. Stevenson a statement regarding the "Open Letter to the Rev. Dr. Hyde." In answer to our inquiry as to the truth of the assertion, so often repeated, that her husband regretted the letter, and that before his death his opinion of Father Damien had undergone a change, Mrs. Stevenson entered an indignantly emphatic denial which is presented on another page. This testimony, we think, should forever settle the matter. The inquiry

was made through the late Charles Warren
Stoddard, who was then contemplating a
new and enlarged edition (since published)
of his own beautiful tribute to Father Damien,
"The Lepers of Molokai." Mrs. Stevenson's
letter is in our possession.

It will further enhance the value and
interest of the present edition of Stevenson's
powerful *apologia* to state that it is an exact
reprint of the original issue, now of extreme
rarity, which has a few corrections in the
writer's own hand. The "Open Letter" was first
printed in a small pamphlet of thirty-two
pages, at Sydney, N. S. W., on March 27, 1890.
Many editions of it had been published before
Mr. Stevenson's death, and it is worth recalling
that he persistently refused to accept pay-
ment from any source for this defence of the
Apostle of Molokai. He once wrote to a
London publisher: "The letter to Dr. Hyde
is yours, or any man's. I will never touch a
penny of remuneration. I do not stick at
murder; I draw the line at cannibalism. I
could not eat a penny roll that piece of bludgeon-
ing brought me."

The use of the Rev. Dr. Rawnsley's exquisite
sonnet, from the collection of poems entitled
"Valete," is with his kind permission.

Notre Dame, Ind.
Jan. 10, 1911.

Statement
by
Mrs. Robert Louis Stevenson.

———

. . . As to the "Open Letter to Dr. Hyde," nothing can make me believe that Louis ever regretted the subject - matter of that piece of writing. To me, up to his last hours, he spoke always in the same strain. His admiration for the work and character of "that saint, that martyr," as he invariably called Father Damien, remained unchanged; and any mention of the cowardly attack on the dead man's memory brought a flush of anger into his face and a fire to his eye that were unmistakable. . . .

Father Damien

An Open Letter to the Reverend Dr. Hyde of
Honolulu from Robert Louis Stevenson

Sydney, February 25, 1890.

SIR, — It may probably occur
to you that we have met,
and visited, and conversed;
on my side with interest. You may
remember that you have done me
several courtesies for which I was pre-
pared to be grateful. But there are
duties which come before gratitude, and
offences which justly divide friends, far
more acquaintances. Your letter to the
Reverend H. B. Gage is a document
which, in my sight, if you had filled me
with bread when I was starving, if you

had sat up to nurse my father when he lay a-dying, would yet absolve me from the bonds of gratitude. You know enough, doubtless, of the process of canonization to be aware that, a hundred years after the death of Damien, there will appear a man charged with the painful office of the *devil's advocate*. After that noble brother of mine, and of all frail clay, shall have lain a century at rest, one shall accuse, one defend him. The circumstance is unusual that the devil's advocate should be a volunteer, should be a member of a sect immediately rival, and should make haste to take upon himself his ugly office ere the bones are cold; unusual, and of a taste which I shall leave my readers free to qualify; unusual, and to me inspiring. If I have at all learned the trade of using words to convey truth and to arouse emotion, you have at last furnished me with a subject. For it is in the interest of all mankind and the cause of public decency in every quarter of the world, not only that Damien should be righted, but that you and your letter should be displayed at length, in their true colors, to the public eye.

To do this properly, I must begin by quoting you at large: I shall then proceed to criticise your utterance from several points of view, divine and human, in the course of which I shall attempt to draw again and with more specification the character of the dead saint whom it has pleased you to vilify: so much being done, I shall say farewell to you forever.

"*Honolulu, Aug. 2, 1889.*

"REV. H. B. GAGE.

"*Dear Brother:*—In answer to your inquiries about Father Damien, I can

only reply that we who knew the man
are surprised at the extravagant news-
paper laudations, as if he was a most
saintly philanthropist. The simple
truth is, he was a coarse, dirty man,
headstrong and bigoted. He was not
sent to Molokai, but went there without orders; did not stay at the leper
settlement (before he became one himself), but circulated freely over the
whole island (less than half the island
is devoted to the lepers), and he came
often to Honolulu. He had no hand
in the reforms and improvements in-
augurated, which were the work of
our Board of Health, as occasion re-
quired and means were provided. He
was not a pure man in his relations
with women, and the leprosy of which
he died should be attributed to his vices
and carelessness. Others have done
much for the lepers, our own ministers,

the government physicians, and so
forth, but never with the catholic
idea of meriting eternal life.

"Yours, ctc.,

"C. M. HYDE."*

To deal fitly with a letter so ex-
traordinary, I must draw at the outset
on my private knowledge of the signa-
tory and his sect. It may offend others;
scarcely you, who have been so busy to
collect, so bold to publish, gossip on
your rivals. And this is perhaps the
moment when I may best explain to
you the character of what you are to
read: I conceive you as a man quite
beyond and below the reticences of
civility: with what measure you mete,
with that shall it be measured you
again; with you at last, I rejoice to
feel the button off the foil and to plunge

*From the Sydney *Presbyterian*, October 26,
1889.

home. And if in aught that I shall say,
I should offend others, your colleagues,
whom I respect and remember with
affection, I can but offer them my re-
gret; I am not free, I am inspired by
the consideration of interests far more
large; and such pain as can be in-
flicted by anything from me must be
indeed trifling when compared with the
pain with which they read your letter.
It is not the hangman, but the criminal,
that brings dishonor on the house.

You belong, sir, to a sect—I believe my
sect, and that in which my ancestors
labored—which has enjoyed, and partly
failed to utilize, an exceptional advan-
tage in the islands of Hawaii. The
first missionaries came; they found the
land already self-purged of its old and
bloody faith; they were embraced, almost on their arrival, with enthusiasm;
what troubles they supported came far

more from whites than from Hawaiians; and to these last they stood (in a rough figure) in the shoes of God. This is not the place to enter into the degree or causes of their failure, such as it is. One element alone is pertinent, and must here be plainly dealt with. In the course of their evangelical calling, they—or too many of them—grew rich. It may be news to you that the houses of missionaries are a cause of mocking on the streets of Honolulu. It will at least be news to you that, when I returned your civil visit, the driver of my cab commented on the size, the taste, and the comfort of your home. It would have been news certainly to myself had any one told me that afternoon that I should live to drag such matter into print. But you see, sir, how you degrade better men to your own level; and it is needful

that those who are to judge betwixt
you and me, betwixt Damien and the
devil's advocate, should understand
your letter to have been penned in a
house which could raise, and that very
justly, the envy and the comments of
the passers-by. I think (to employ a
phrase of yours, which I admire) it
"should be attributed" to you that
you have never visited the scene of
Damien's life and death. If you had, and
had recalled it, and looked about your
pleasant rooms, even your pen perhaps
would have been stayed.

Your sect (and, remember, as far as
any sect avows me, it is mine) has
not done ill in a worldly sense in the
Hawaiian Kingdom. When calamity
befell their innocent parishioners, when
leprosy descended and took root in the
Eight Islands, a *quid pro quo* was to
be looked for. To that prosperous mis-

sion, and to you, as one of its adorn-
ments, God had sent at last an oppor-
tunity. I know I am touching here
upon a nerve acutely sensitive. I know
that others of your colleagues look back
on the inertia of your church, and the
intrusive and decisive heroism of Damien, with something almost to be
called remorse. I am sure it is so with
yourself; I am persuaded your letter
was inspired by a certain envy, not
essentially ignoble, and the one human
trait to be espied in that performance.
You were thinking of the lost chance,
the past day; of that which should
have been conceived and was not; of
the service due and not rendered. *Time
was*, said the voice in your ear, in your
pleasant room, as you sat raging and
writing; and if the words written were
base beyond parallel, the rage, I am
happy to repeat—it is the only com-

pliment I shall pay you—the rage was
almost virtuous. But, sir, when we
have failed, and another has succeeded;
when we have stood by, and another
has stepped in; when we sit and grow
bulky in our charming mansions, and
a plain, uncouth peasant steps into the
battle, under the eyes of God, and suc-
cors the afflicted, and consoles the
dying, and is himself afflicted in his
turn, and dies upon the field of honor
—the battle can not be retrieved as
your unhappy irritation has suggested.
It is a lost battle, and lost forever.
One thing remained to you in your
defeat—some rags of common honor;
and these you have made haste to cast
away.

Common honor; not the honor of
having done anything right, but the
honor of not having done aught con-
spicuously foul; the honor of the inert:

that was what remained to you. We
are not all expected to be Damiens; a
man may conceive his duty more nar-
rowly, he may love his comforts better;
and none will cast a stone at him for
that. But will a gentleman of your
reverend profession allow me an ex-
ample from the fields of gallantry?
When two gentlemen compete for the
favor of a lady, and the one succeeds
and the other is rejected, and (as will
sometimes happen) matter damaging to
the successful rival's credit reaches the
ear of the defeated, it is held by plain
men of no pretensions that his mouth
is, in the circumstance, almost neces-
sarily closed. Your church and Damien's were in Hawaii upon a rivalry
to do well: to help, to edify, to set
divine examples. You having (in one
huge instance) failed, and Damien succeeded, I marvel it should not have

occurred to you that you were doomed
to silence; that when you had been
outstripped in that high rivalry, and
sat inglorious in the midst of your well-
being, in your pleasant room—and
Damien, crowned with glories and hor-
rors, toiled and rotted in that pigsty
of his under the cliffs of Kalawao—you,
the elect who would not, were the last
man on earth to collect and propagate
gossip on the volunteer who would and
did.

I think I see you—for I try to see you
in the flesh as I write these sentences—
I think I see you leap at the word pigsty, a hyperbolical expression at the
best. "He had no hand in the reforms," he was "a coarse, dirty man";
these were your own words; and you
may think it possible that I am come
to support you with fresh evidence.
In a sense it is even so. Damien has

been too much depicted with a conventional halo and conventional features; so drawn by men who perhaps had not the eye to remark or the pen to express the individual; or who perhaps were only blinded and silenced by generous admiration, such as I partly envy for myself—such as you, if your soul were enlightened, would envy on your bended knees. It is the least defect of such a method of portraiture that it makes the path easy for the devil's advocate, and leaves for the misuse of the slanderer a considerable field of truth. For the truth that is suppressed by friends is the readiest weapon of the enemy. The world, in your despite, may perhaps owe you something, if your letter be the means of substituting once for all a credible likeness for a wax abstraction. For, if that world at all remember you, on the day when

Damien of Molokai shall be named
Saint, it will be in virtue of one work:
your letter to the Reverend H. B. Gage.
You may ask on what authority I
speak. It was my inclement destiny
to become acquainted, not with Damien, but with Dr. Hyde. When I
visited the lazaretto, Damien was already in his resting grave. But such
information as I have, I gathered on the
spot in conversation with those who
knew him well and long: some indeed
who revered his memory; but others
who had sparred and wrangled with
him, who beheld him with no halo,
who perhaps regarded him with small
respect, and through whose unpre-
pared and scarcely partial communica-
tions the plain, human features of the
man shone on me convincingly. These
gave me what knowledge I possess;
and I learned it in that scene where it

could be most completely and sensitively understood — Kalawao, which you have never visited, about which you have never so much as endeavored to inform yourself: for, brief as your letter is, you have found the means to stumble into that confession. "*Less than one-half* of the island," you say, "is devoted to the lepers." Molokai — "*Molokai ahina*," the "gray," lofty, and most desolate island—along all its northern side plunges a front of precipice into a sea of unusual profundity. This range of cliff is, from east to west, the true end and frontier of the island. Only in one spot there projects into the ocean a certain triangular and rugged down, grassy, stony, windy, and rising in the midst into a hill with a dead crater: the whole bearing to the cliff that overhangs it, somewhat the same relation

as a bracket to a wall. With this hint,
you will now be able to pick out the
leper station on a map; you will be
able to judge how much of Molokai
is thus cut off between the surf and
precipice, whether less than a half, or
less than a quarter, or a fifth, or a
tenth—or, say, a twentieth; and the
next time you burst into print you will
be in a position to share with us the
issue of your calculations.

I imagine you to be one of those per-
sons who talk with cheerfulness of that
place which oxen and wainropes could
not drag you to behold. You, who do
not even know its situation on the map,
probably denounce sensational descrip-
tions, stretching your limbs the while
in your pleasant parlor on Beretania
Street. When I was pulled ashore there
one early morning, there sat with me
in the boat two Sisters, bidding fare-

well (in humble imitation of Damien) to the lights and joys of human life. One of these wept silently; I could not withhold myself from joining her. Had you been there, it is my belief that nature would have triumphed even in you; and as the boat drew but a little nearer, and you beheld the stairs crowded with abominable deformations of our common manhood, and saw yourself landing in the midst of such a population as only now and then surrounds us in the horror of a nightmare—what a haggard eye would you have rolled over your reluctant shoulder toward the house on Beretania Street! Had you gone on; had you found every fourth face a blot upon the landscape; had you visited the hospital and seen the butt-ends of human beings lying there almost unrecognizable, but still breathing, still

thinking, still remembering; you would
have understood that life in the lazaretto is an ordeal from which the nerves
of a man's spirit shrink, even as his
eye quails under the brightness of the
sun; you would have felt it was (even
to-day) a pitiful place to visit and a
hell to dwell in. It is not the fear of
possible infection. That seems a little
thing when compared with the pain,
the pity, and the disgust of the visitor's
surroundings, and the atmosphere of
affliction, disease, and physical disgrace
in which he breathes. I do not think
I am a man more than usually timid;
but I never recall the days and nights
I spent upon that island promontory
(eight days and seven nights), without heartfelt thankfulness that I am
somewhere else. I find in my diary
that I speak of my stay as "a grind-
ing experience": I have once jotted in

the margin, "*Harrowing* is the word";
and when the *Mokolii* bore me at last
toward the outer world, I kept re-
peating to myself, with a new concep-
tion of their pregnancy, those simple
words of the song—

> "'Tis the most distressful country
> That ever yet was seen."

And observe: that which I saw and
suffered from was a settlement, purged,
bettered, beautified; the new village
built, the hospital and the Bishop's-
Home excellently arranged; the Sisters,
the doctor, and the missionaries all in-
defatigable in their noble tasks. It was
a different place when Damien came
there, and made his great renunciation,
and slept that first night under a tree
amidst his rotting brethren: alone
with pestilence; and looking forward
(with what courage, with what pitiful sinkings of dread, God only knows)

to a lifetime of dressing sores and stumps.

You will say, perhaps, I am too sensitive, that sights as painful abound in cancer hospitals and are confronted daily by doctors and nurses. I have long learned to admire and envy the doctors and the nurses. But there is no cancer hospital so large and populous as Kalawao and Kalaupapa; and in such a matter every fresh case, like every inch of length in the pipe of an organ, deepens the note of the impression; for what daunts the onlooker is that monstrous sum of human suffering by which he stands surrounded. Lastly, no doctor or nurse is called upon to enter once for all the doors of that gehenna; they do not say farewell, they need not abandon hope, on its sad threshold; they but go for a time to their high calling; and can look forward as they go to relief, to recreation, and to rest. But Damien shut to with his own hand the doors of his own sepulchre.

I shall now extract three passages from my diary at Kalawao.

A. "Damien is dead and already somewhat ungratefully remembered in the field of his labors and sufferings. 'He was a good man, but very officious,' says one. Another tells me he had fallen (as other priests so easily do) into something of the ways and habits of thought of a Kanaka; but he had the wit to recognize the fact, and the good sense to laugh at" [over] "it. A plain man it seems he was; I can not find he was a popular."

B. "After Ragsdale's death" [Ragsdale was a famous Luna, or overseer, of the unruly settlement] "there followed a brief term of office by Father

Damien which served only to publish
the weakness of that noble man. He
was rough in his ways, and he had no
control. Authority was relaxed; Damien's life was threatened, and he was
soon eager to resign."

C. "Of Damien I begin to have an
idea. He seems to have been a man
of the peasant class, certainly of the
peasant type: shrewd, ignorant and
bigoted; yet with an open mind, and
capable of receiving and digesting a
reproof if it were bluntly administered;
superbly generous in the least thing as
well as in the greatest, and as ready to
give his last shirt (although not without human grumbling) as he had been
to sacrifice his life; essentially indiscreet
and officious, which made him a trouble-
some colleague; domineering in all his
ways, which made him incurably un-
popular with the Kanakas, but yet

destitute of real authority, so that his
boys laughed at him, and he must carry
out his wishes by the means of bribes.
He learned to have a mania for doctor-
ing; and set up the Kanakas against
the remedies of his regular rivals: perhaps (if anything matter at all in the
treatment of such a disease) the worst
thing that he did, and certainly the
easiest.   The best and worst of the man
appear very plainly in his dealings with
Mr. Chapman's money; he had original-
ly laid it out" [intended to lay it out]
"entirely for the benefit of Catholics,
and even so not wisely; but after a
long, plain talk, he admitted his error
fully, and revised the list.   The sad state
of the boys' home is in part the result
of his lack of control; in part, of his
own slovenly ways and false ideas of
hygiene.   Brother officials used to call
it 'Damien's Chinatown.'   'Well,' they

would say, 'your Chinatown keeps
growing.' And he would laugh with
perfect good nature, and adhere to his
errors with perfect obstinacy. So much
I have gathered of truth about this
plain, noble human brother and Father
of ours; his imperfections are the traits
of his face, by which we know him for
our fellow; his martyrdom and his ex-
ample nothing can lessen or annul; and
only a person here on the spot can
properly appreciate their greatness.'

I have set down these private passages, as you perceive, without correc-
tion; thanks to you, the public has
them in their bluntness. They are almost a list of the man's faults, for it is
rather these that I was seeking, with
his virtues, with the heroic profile of his
life, I and the world were already suf-
ficiently acquainted. I was besides a
little suspicious of Catholic testimony;

in no ill sense, but merely because Damien's admirers and disciples were the
least likely to be critical. I know you
will be more suspicious still; and the
facts set down above were one and all
collected from the lips of Protestants
who had opposed the Father in his life.
Yet I am strangely deceived, or they
build up the image of a man, with all
his weaknesses, essentially heroic, and
alive with rugged honesty, generosity,
and mirth.

Take it for what it is, rough private
jottings of the worst sides of Damien's
character, collected from the lips of
those who had labored with and (in
your own phrase) "knew the man,"—
though I question whether Damien
would have said that he knew you.
Take it, and observe with wonder how
well you were served by your gossips,
how ill by your intelligence and sympa-

thy; in how many points of fact we
are at one, and how widely our appre-
ciations vary. There is something
wrong here; either with you or me.
It is possible, for instance, that you,
who seem to have so many ears in
Kalawao, had heard of the affair of
Mr. Chapman's money, and were singly
struck by Damien's intended wrong-
doing. I was struck with that also,
and set it fairly down; but I was struck
much more by the fact that he had the
honesty of mind to be convinced. I
may here tell you that it was a long
business; that one of his colleagues sat
with him late into the night, multiply-
ing arguments and accusations; that
the Father listened as usual with "perfect good nature and perfect obstinacy";
but at the last, when he was persuaded
— "Yes," said he, "I am very much
obliged to you; you have done me a

service; it would have been a theft."
There are many (not Catholics merely)
who require their heroes and saints to
be infallible; to these the story will be
painful; not to the true lovers, patrons,
and servants of mankind.

And I take it, this is a type of our
division: that you are one of those
who have an eye for faults and failures;
that you take a pleasure to find and
publish them; and that, having found
them, you make haste to forget the
overvailing virtues and the real success
which had alone introduced them to
your knowledge. It is a dangerous
frame of mind. That you may understand how dangerous, and into what
a situation it has already brought you,
we will (if you please) go hand-in-hand
through the different phrases of your
letter, and candidly examine each from

the point of view of its truth, its
appositeness, and its charity.

Damien was *coarse*.

It is very possible. You make us sorry
for the lepers, who had only a coarse
old peasant for their friend and Father.
But you, who were so refined, why
were you not there to cheer them with
the lights of culture? Or may I remind
you that we have some reason to doubt
if John the Baptist were genteel; and,
in the case of Peter, on whose career
you doubtless dwell approvingly in the
pulpit, no doubt at all that he was a
"coarse, headstrong" fisherman! Yet,
even in our Protestant Bibles, Peter is
called Saint.

Damien was *dirty*.

He was. Think of the poor lepers
annoyed with this dirty comrade! But
the clean Dr. Hyde was at his food in
a fine house.

Damien was *headstrong*.

I believe you are right again; and I thank God for his strong head and heart.

Damien was *bigoted*.

I am not fond of bigots myself, because they are not fond of me. But what is meant by bigotry, that we should regard it as a blemish in a priest? Damien believed his own religion with the simplicity of a peasant or a child; as I would I could suppose that you do. For this, I wonder at him some way off; and had that been his only character, should have avoided him in life. But the point of interest in Damien, which has caused him to be so much talked about and made him at last the subject of your pen and mine, was that, in him, his bigotry, his intense and narrow faith, wrought potently for good, and strengthened

him to be one of the world's heroes
and exemplars.

Damien *was not sent to Molokai,
but went there without orders.*

Is this a misreading? or do you really
mean the words for blame? I have
heard Christ, in the pulpits of our
Church, held up for imitation on the
ground that His sacrifice was volun-
tary. Does Dr. Hyde think otherwise?

Damien *did not stay at the settlement,* etc.

It is true he was allowed many in-
dulgences. Am I to understand that
you blame the Father for profiting by
these, or the officers for granting them?
In either case, it is a mighty Spartan
standard to issue from the house on
Beretania Street; and I am convinced
you will find yourself with few sup-
porters.

Damien *had no hand in the reforms,*
etc.

I think even you will admit that I
have already been frank in my descrip-
tion of the man I am defending; but
before I take you up upon this head,
I will be franker still, and tell you that
perhaps nowhere in the world can a
man taste a more pleasurable sense of
contrast than when he passes from Damien's "Chinatown" at Kalawao to the
beautiful Bishop's-Home at Kalaupapa.
At this point, in my desire to make
all fair for you, I will break my rule
and adduce Catholic testimony. Here
is a passage from my diary about my
visit to the Chinatown, from which
you will see how it is (even now) regarded by its own officials: "We went
round all the dormitories, refectories,
etc.—dark and dingy enough, with a
superficial cleanliness, which he" [Mr.

Dutton, the lay brother] "did not seek
to defend. 'It is almost decent,' said
he; 'the Sisters will make that all right
when we get them here.'" And yet I
gathered it was already better since
Damien was dead, and far better than
when he was there alone and had his
own (not always excellent) way. I
have now come far enough to meet
you on a common ground of fact; and
I tell you that, to a mind not prejudiced
by jealousy, all the reforms of the Lazaretto, and even those which he most
vigorously opposed, are properly the
work of Damien. They are the evidence
of his success; they are what his heroism provoked from the reluctant and
the careless. Many were before him in
the field; Mr. Meyer, for instance, of
whose faithful work we hear too little;
there have been many since; and some
had more worldly wisdom, though none

had more devotion, than our saint. Before his day, even you will confess, they had effected little. It was his part, by one striking act of martyrdom, to direct all men's eyes on that distressful country. At a blow, and with the price of his life, he made the place illustrious and public. And, that, if you will consider largely, was the one reform needful; pregnant of all that should succeed. It brought money; it brought (best individual addition of them all) the Sisters; it brought supervision, for public opinion and public interest landed with the man at Kalawao. If ever any man brought reforms, and died to bring them, it was he. There is not a clean cup or towel in the Bishop's-Home but dirty Damien washed it.

Damien *was not a pure man in his relations with women, etc.*

How do you know that? Is this
the nature of the conversation in that
house on Beretania Street which the
cabman envied, driving past?—racy
details of the misconduct of the poor
peasant priest, toiling under the cliffs
of Molokai?

Many have visited the station before me; they seem not to have heard
the rumor. When I was there I heard
many shocking tales, for my informants
were men speaking with the plainness
of the laity; and I heard plenty of
complaints of Damien. Why was this
never mentioned? and how came it to
you in the retirement of your clerical
parlor?

But I must not even seem to deceive
you. This scandal, when I read it in
your letter, was not new to me. I had
heard it once before; and I must tell
you how. There came to Samoa a man

from Honolulu; he, in a public-house
on the beach, volunteered the statement
that Damien had "contracted the disease from having connection with the
female lepers"; and I find a joy in telling
you how the report was welcomed in
a public-house. A man sprang to his
feet; I am not at liberty to give his
name, but from what I heard I doubt
if you would care to have him to dinner
in Beretania Street. "You miserable little——," (here is a word I dare not print,
it would so shock your ears). "You
miserable little ——," he cried," if the
story were a thousand times true, can't
you see you are a million times a lower
—— for daring to repeat it?" I wish
it could be told of you that when the
report reached you in your house, perhaps after family worship, you had
found in your soul enough holy anger
to receive it with the same expressions;

ay, even with that one which I dare
not print; it would not need to have
been blotted away, like Uncle Toby's
oath, by the tears of the recording
angel; it would have been counted to
you for your brightest righteousness.
But you have deliberately chosen the
part of the man from Honolulu, and
you have played it with improvements
of your own. The man from Honolulu
—miserable, leering creature—communi-
cated the tale to a rude knot of beach-
combing drinkers in a public-house,
where (I will so far agree with your
temperance opinions) man is not always at his noblest; and the man
from Honolulu had himself been drinking—drinking, we may charitably fancy,
to excess. It was to your "Dear
Brother, the Reverend H. B. Gage,"
that you chose to communicate the
sickening story; and the blue ribbon

which adorns your portly bosom for-
bids me to allow you the extenuating
plea that you were drunk when it was
done. Your "dear brother"—a brother
indeed—made haste to deliver up your
letter (as a means of grace, perhaps)
to the religious papers; where, after
many months, I found and read and
wondered at it; and whence I have
now reproduced it for the wonder of
others. And you and your dear brother
have, by this cycle of operations, built
up a contrast very edifying to examine
in detail. The man whom you would
not care to have to dinner, on the one
side; on the other, the Reverend Dr.
Hyde and the Reverend H. B. Gage; the
Apia bar-room, the Honolulu manse.

But I fear you scarce appreciate how
you appear to your fellowmen: and
to bring it home to you, I will suppose
your story to be true I will suppose

—and God forgive me for supposing it
—that Damien faltered and stumbled
in his narrow path of duty; I will suppose that, in the horror of his isolation,
perhaps in the fever of incipient disease,
he, who was doing so much more than
he had sworn, failed in the letter of his
priestly oath—he, who was so much a
better man than either you or me, who
did what we have never dreamed of
daring—he too tasted of our common
frailty. "O Iago, the pity of it!" The
least tender should be moved to tears;
the most incredulous to prayer. And
all that you could do was to pen your
letter to the Reverend H. B. Gage!

Is it growing at all clear to you what
a picture you have drawn of your own
heart? I will try yet once again to
make it clearer. You had a father:
suppose this tale were about him, and
some informant brought it to you,

proof in hand: I am not making too
high an estimate of your emotional
nature when I suppose you would re-
gret the circumstance? that you would
feel the tale of frailty the more keenly
since it shamed the author of your
days? and that the last thing you
would do would be to publish it in the
religious press? Well, the man who
tried to do what Damien did is my
Father, and the Father of the man in
the Apia bar, and the Father of all
who love goodness; and he was your
Father, too, if God had given you grace
to see it.

Father Damien.

———

NO golden dome shines over Damien's sleep:
  A leper's grave upon a leprous strand,
    Where hope is dead, and hand must shrink
      from hand,
Where cataracts wail towards a moaning deep,
And frowning purple cliffs in mercy keep
    All wholesome life at distance, hath God
      planned
  For him who led his saintly hero band,
And died a shepherd of Christ's exiled sheep.

O'er Damien's dust the broad skies bend for
    dome,
  Stars burn for golden letters, and the sea
    Shall roll perpetual anthem round his rest:
For Damien made the charnel-house life's home,
  Matched love with death; and Damien's name
    shall be
  A glorious benediction, world-possest.
                H. D. RAWNSLEY.

A Companion Book.

("The Lepers of Molokai," by Charles Warren Stoddard.)

AVE MARIA PRESS, NOTRE DAME, IND.

"Robert Louis Stevenson's 'Open Letter to the Rev. Dr. Hyde of Honolulu' has pilloried the defamer of the martyr for all time"; in Charles Warren Stoddard's transporting volume, the prologue to which is here presented, the martyr's memory is forever hallowed.

Prologue.

THE afternoon was waning in the tropical seaport; already the heat was tempered and the glare softened by the humidity of the slowly approaching dusk. A little while and the sun would sink silently into the immeasurable abyss beyond the waves, and the brief, delicious twilight, bathed for a moment only in the splendor of the afterglow, would adorn itself with clusters of trembling stars.

At such an hour, beguiled with reveries and soothed by the exquisite fragrance that exhales at dew-fall, I was startled by a piercing cry that seemed the last agonizing protest of a riven heart. Not one voice only broke upon the stillness, but another and another, and yet another, until a chorus of despair rang shrilly over the low-roofed cottages in the grove that stood between me and the not far-distant shore. With no little emotion I hurried seaward, and speedily overtook a melancholy procession of weeping

women following a few silent people,
who were being conducted with decent
haste toward the esplanade of Honolulu.

The miserable beings, with a dazed
look of lingering death in their fearful
countenances, were soon disposed on the
deck of a small outward-bound craft;
and then, in the few moments that inter-
vened between the casting off of the
shoreline and the sudden impulse of
the little steamer as she swung about in
mid-stream, and made bravely for the
mouth of the harbor, the pitiful wail of
men, women and children was renewed.
Those grouped upon the extreme edge
of the wharf were wringing their hands
over the water, while rivers of tears
coursed down their ashen cheeks. The
others, upon the deck of the departing
vessel, brooded for a time as in dull
agony, but anon an unearthly cry rang
over the tranquil sea: it was their long
farewell.

The sun, just touching the horizon,
seemed to pause for a moment, while
the great deep burst into a sheet of
flame; tongues of fire darted and played
among the wavelets as they tossed in

the evening breeze; and the broad rays shot from cloud to cloud, painting them with glory, and crowning the peaks of the beautiful island with red-gold. Even the palm-trees were gilded, and their plumes glistened as they swayed rhythmically to the low melody of the tide that ebbed beneath them.

So faded that ill-starred bark like a mote in the shimmering sea. A few moments only, and the splendor died away—the twilight glow of the tropics is as brief as it is intense—and the sudden coming of night drew a veil over a picture that, though frequent, is nevertheless painful to the least sympathetic observer.

Darkness had come; the silence that came with it was broken only by the splash of ripples under the bow of some passing canoe, or the low moan of the water upon the distant reef. But the mourners were still crouching upon the edge of the dock, whence their eyes had caught the last glimpse of the fading forms of those whom they were never again to behold in the flesh; for those despairing but unresisting souls, swallowed up in the transfiguration of the sunset,

were lepers, snatched from the breast
of sympathy and from the arms of love,
doomed to the hopeless degradation of
everlasting banishment, and borne in
the night to that dim island whose
melancholy shores are the sole refuge
of these hostages to death: an island
as solitary, as silent, as serene as dream-
land—mournful Molokai.